THE MISSING MONSTER CARD

www.raintreepublishers.co.uk
Visit our website to find out
more information about
Raintree books.

To order:
☎ Phone 0845 6044371
🖨 Fax +44 (0) 1865 312263
📧 Email myorders@raintreepublishers.co.uk

Customers from outside the UK please telephone +44 1865 312262

Raintree is an imprint of Capstone Global Library Limited, a company incorporated
in England and Wales having its registered office at 7 Pilgrim Street, London,
EC4V 6LB – Registered company number: 6695582

Text © Stone Arch Books 2010
First published in hardback and paperback in the United Kingdom by
Capstone Global Library in 2011
The moral rights of the proprietor have been asserted.

UK editor: Siân Smith
Graphic Designer: Emily Harris
Art Director: Bob Lentz
Production Specialist: Michelle Biedscheid
Illustrations by Rémy Simard
Originated by Capstone Global Library Ltd
Printed and bound in China by South China Printing Company Ltd

ISBN 978 1 406 22548 8 (hardback)
15 14 13 12 11
10 9 8 7 6 5 4 3 2 1

ISBN 978 1 406 22553 2 (paperback)
15 14 13 12 11
10 9 8 7 6 5 4 3 2 1

British Library Cataloguing in Publication Data
Mortensen, Lori. The missing monster card. -- (My first graphic novel)
741.5-dc22
A full catalogue record for this book is available from the British Library.

THE MISSING MONSTER CARD

by Lori Mortensen

illustrated by Rémy Simard

HOW TO READ A GRAPHIC NOVEL

Graphic novels are easy to read. Boxes called panels show you how to follow the story. Look at the panels from left to right and top to bottom.

Read the word boxes and speech bubbles from left to right as well. Don't forget the sound and action words in the pictures.

The pictures and the words work together to tell the whole story.

Every Saturday, Ethan went to Ryan's house.
They played Monster Cards for hours.

Ethan couldn't wait for this Saturday. He had a new card. And not just any new card.

The most priceless Monster Card you could get.

That night, Ethan put the card in his coat pocket.

The next morning, Ethan grabbed his coat and called Ryan.

He raced to Ryan's house.

Ethan and Ryan sat down on the floor. They spread out all of their Monster Cards.

Ethan reached inside his pocket. It wasn't there.

Ethan checked his pockets. They were all empty.

Ethan could not find his new card.

They slowly walked back to Ethan's house. Ethan stepped on some chewing gum. Ryan found an old sweet on the floor.

Ryan also found a penny.

Ethan found food wrappers.

They searched everywhere. But they didn't find Ethan's card.

Ethan went inside and hung up his coat.

Ethan looked under his bed. Ryan looked under the cushions on the sofa.

They both looked in the rubbish bin.

But Ethan's card was gone.

Then Ethan had an idea. He got a pencil and wrote down some clues.

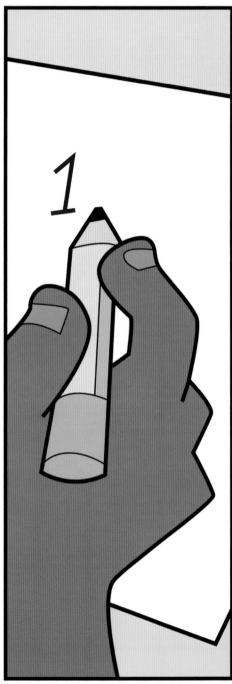

He wrote down what he had done before he
went to Ryan's house.

Ethan raced to the kitchen table. He looked under the newspaper.

But the card wasn't there.

Ethan looked at the clues again. Being a detective was hard work.

Ethan grabbed his brown coat. Something fell
out of the pocket.

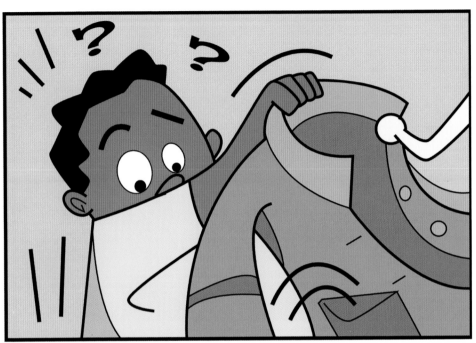

His new Monster Card was in the pocket of his brown coat, not his blue coat!

Lori Mortensen is a multi-published children's author who writes fiction and non-fiction on all sorts of subjects. When she's not typing away at the keyboard, she enjoys making cheesy bread rolls, gardening, and spending time with her family.

ABOUT THE ILLUSTRATOR

Artist Rémy Simard began his career as an illustrator in 1980. Today he creates computer-generated illustrations for a large variety of people. He has also written and illustrated more than 30 children's books in both French and English, including *Monsieur Noir et Blanc*, a finalist for Canada's Governor's Prize. To relax, Rémy likes to race around on his motorbike. Rémy lives with his two sons and a cat named Billy.

GLOSSARY

CLUES things that help you find the answer to a mystery

DETECTIVES people who try to solve mysteries or crimes

MYSTERY something that is hard to understand or explain

PRICELESS so valuable that no amount of money could buy it

SEARCHED looked for something

DISCUSSION QUESTIONS

1. Do you have any items that you think are priceless? Discuss what makes these items so special to you.

2. Every Saturday, Ryan and Ethan get together to play Monster Cards. Talk about an activity that you would like to do every week.

3. Do you want to be a detective? Why or why not?

WRITING PROMPTS

1. Lots of people collect things. If you had to collect something, what would it be? Write a paragraph about your collection.

2. Pretend you lost the most valuable thing you own. What would you do? Write a paragraph describing your detective plan.

3. Were you able to solve the card mystery? Look through the book again. List any clues you see that would help you solve the mystery.

MY 1ST GRAPHIC NOVEL®

THE 1ST STEP INTO GRAPHIC NOVELS

These books are the perfect introduction to the world of graphic novels. Each story uses familiar topics, repeating patterns, and core vocabulary words appropriate for a beginning reader. Combine an entertaining story with comic book panels, exciting action elements, and bright colours, and a graphic novel is born!